A LARGE MACC. AND A GLASS OF WATE

The sun was beating down fiercely as he walked along South Terrace into town. The glare before his eyes seemed almost to flare and bounce back, imprinting all he saw onto his mind like a high contrast photographic image. Mid-tones were going. Visual subtleties disappearing, burnt out of existence. Blocks of light and dark remained: the monolith of the hospital; the moving silhouette of a passerby; a meat delivery van being unloaded, the red slabs a more saturated colour than he'd ever seen before. He needed a coffee.

He remembered reading somewhere that the colour of blood depended on the amount of oxygen in it. A textbook from high school? All about the heart. Left and right ventricles. Blood going into and coming out from. De-oxygenated blood was darker, almost purple, whereas re-oxygenated blood was lighter, a sort of strawberry red. Or was it the other way around? Anyway, oxygen was the key to it all. The determining factor.

He felt in his shirt pocket for the sunglasses. Not there. In the other shirt of course, the one he'd tossed on the floor yesterday afternoon. Another hot one. The days recently felt as if they were merging into one vague expanse where heat and light were the only constants. Summer. A Fremantle summer. Night and dark existed also - he couldn't deny it - but they passed too quickly to have any real meaning. It couldn't just be explained by the fact that one went to sleep at night, and that consciousness was turned off for a few hours. Time was compressed after the sun went down. It expanded when the sun came up. He wondered if any studies had been done on this phenomenon.

He squinted his eyes as he waited at the lights. Traffic was heavy, and cars were banking up the Terrace and Norfolk Street. The drivers and passengers were all wearing sunglasses, and he wondered what colours their eyes were behind the darkness. Brown eyes were the most common, then green, then blue. He supposed they all saw the world the same way. He thought of the pink eyes of albinos. They were more sensitive to bright light, but could they also receive a different sort of message from things around them? In a softer, kinder light did they perceive hidden nuances or emanations that escaped the blunt vision of others?

A black dog came and stood beside him. It joined his space. It thumped his leg with a wagging tail and looked up. It had black eyes. This seemed fair enough. Dogs have monochrome vision. The aesthetics of eye colour were a non-event to them. A waste of time. A black and white view of things prevailed in their world. Skin colours become shades of grey. Blood would be black. Could dogs pick the difference in colour between de-oxygenated and re-oxygenated blood? Shades of black? He pondered this as they crossed the burning road together and walked toward the markets.

A juggler was performing in the space outside the market entrance. A large crowd had gathered. People were pressing in to get a good view of the act. He joined the throng, the dog following closely. He could feel its wet nose on his ankles sometimes as he made his way forward. Flaming brands, that looked like the sticks from a bass drum, were being thrown into the air, caught, manipulated, and tossed up again. A thick black smoke rose from them whenever they were momentarily still. He tried to watch them at that brief static point at the top of each throw. The instant before they fell to earth again. Frozen flames in the hot blue sky. That moment. Then.

The dog licked his foot and he took this as the sign to go. They made their way through the still enraptured crowd and were abruptly back on the footpath again. Tourists and locals were coming from or going to the zone. Straw hats, more sunglasses, and tropical designs on clothing. Blinding white shirts jumped out and assaulted his seeing eyes. Old ladies in wheelchairs being pushed by faithful retainers. Rastafarian dreads. Babies in prams. Old Italian men in conviviality. Exuberant teenagers and young lovers. A Morrocan friend waved to in passing. Family groups. He suddenly felt as though he was part of a slow motion sequence in a film about ethnographic diversity. Alien beings would have a microcosmic view of humankind if they managed to tape this show and replay it. Beamed from one of the most isolated cities on the planet Earth. In the constellation of the Milky Way.

They were almost there. Out of the sun and the crush. The rush of travelling humanity, and too much information to take in. His eyes were starting to hurt. He thought about visual overload, and whether or not this might somehow be accentuated by the hole in the ozone layer and the brightness of the light, or if it was still simply a matter of just seeing too much. The world was all about.

Seized by a moment of intense curiosity he stopped walking and looked down at the dog. Not near enough. He crouched down, stroked the dog's head, and then let his eyes gaze closely at the black coat of its back. He tried to merge his eyes into the blackness. The absence of light and colour. A rest for the optics. The dog licked his hand. He attempted to unfocus his eyes, but that didn't seem to work either. The dog was a healthy specimen and it had a shiny coat. The slight reflectance, the almost glossy sheen, was a distraction and a visual event in itself. No rest in that quarter. He thanked the dog anyway and stood up again, blinking into the glare. The dog, possibly blessed with ESP, trotted off towards Gino's coffee shop. He followed it there.

Into the beckoning shade. Cool and muted light. As his eyes relaxed auditory and olfactory senses came alive. A chink of cups and saucers. That smell of fresh coffee. Clinking of glasses. A hubbub of voices. The expected ambience. Expected, but reassuring nonetheless. He joined the queue at the counter, and scanned the blackboard on the back wall listing the various coffees and hot drinks. It was a part of his own ritual, almost a reflex action now, that happened every time he came into Gino's. He'd look up at the blackboard, fascinated by the variations possible on a cup of coffee: small macchiato, large macchiato, Shirley's macchiato, expresso, short black, long black (double shot), mocha, Vienna, affogato, latte, flat white, cappuccino. Decaf, skim milk and soy milk variations of most were "available on request". Had there ever really been such a thing as a "simple cup of coffee"? The standard article. Does there exist somewhere in that misty region of Platonic ideals a perfect cup of coffee sitting steaming on a perfect table? How do they drink coffee in Brazil?

"What would you like?" asked the coffee maker's offsider. "A large macc. and a glass of water" he replied. The Large Macchiato. A good blast of coffee, enough to make you wake up for the second time in a day. He paid the money, picked up the coffee and water, and looked for an empty table. There was nothing inside so he walked out into the heat and light again, and found a table near the busy street. The dog was sitting underneath the table. It appeared to be waiting for him. He greeted the hound and sat down.

A newspaper was lying on the table. Underneath it a pair of sunglasses. He tried them on. A perfect fit. He took a taste of the coffee and looked at the movement all around. A girl in a red dress crossed the street followed closely by a young man in red trousers. Black to the dog. We're all of us meat, but seventy percent water as well. And a certain amount of spirit. He took a deep breath and settled back into the chair. Thought about light and dark. Synchronicity and coincidence. And summertime in the city of Fremantle.

High Street Mall paving / 2001

High Street footpath / 2000

Looking to the railway station and harbour / Market Street / 2001

James Street / Mid 90's

'Leeuwin' / Fremantle harbour / 2001

Letterboxes / Central Fremantle / Mid 90's

Barber's shop angel / Market Street / Early 90's

At the Round House / 2001

Fremantle Markets entrance / Mid 90's

Street performer / outside the Fremantle Markets / 2000

Jazz band / outside the Sail & Anchor Hotel / 2001

Dragon / St Patrick's Presbytery / 2001

Gargoyle / High Street / 2001

20

Commemorative Cross and Proclamation Tree / Adelaide Street / 2001

National Hotel / High Street / 2001

Near the Fremantle Markets / Mid 90's

Street performer / outside the Fremantle Markets / 2001

Blessing of the Fleet procession / 2000

'Freo Samba' drummers / South Terrace / 2000

Religious icons / Queen Street shop / 2000

Bus queue / Queen Street / 2000

Cafè / South Terrace / Late 90's

Car park / Collie Street / Late 90's

The old woolstores / Parry Street / 2000

Buskers' Festival / South Terrace / 2001

32

William Street / 2000

St John's Square / 2001

Wedding reception dance / East Fremantle Tennis Club / 2001

Family / Fremantle Markets / Mid 90's

Cafè / South Terrace / 2001

Cafè / South Terrace / 2000

Dancing / South Terrace / Late 90's

Boys and puppet / Collie Street / 2001

South Terrace Piazza / 2001

William Street / 2000

42

Looking through Gino's window / South Terrace / Mid 90's

Outside Old Papa's cafè / South Terrace / Early 90's

South Terrace / Mid 90's

High Street Mall / 2001

Gino's window / South Terrace / 2001

Cafè / South Terrace / Mid 90's

Westgate Mall / 2001

Back of shops / Paddy Troy Mall / 2001

DIRECTORY

Shop 1	Vacant
Shop 2	August Moon Asian Restaurant
Shop 3	Zodiax
Shop 4	Hearts n' Halos
Shop 5	Weekends Boutique
Shop 6	Tara Fashions & Alterations
Shop 7	Adams Hourglass Jewellers
Shop 8	Womens Cancer Prevention Unit
Shop 9	
Shop 10	Jeans West
Shop 11	

Buskers / High Street Mall / 2001

Market Street / Mid 90's

Buskers' Festival / South Terrace / 2001

Street performer / South Terrace / 2001

Freo Festival / South Terrace / Late 90's

Juggler / High Street Mall / Late 90's

Parade / Freo Festival / South Terrace / 2000

Parade / Freo Festival / Market Street / 2000

Medusa head / South Fremantle / Early 90's

Street performer / outside the Sail & Anchor Hotel / Late 90's

Street performer / outside the Sail & Anchor Hotel / South Terrace / 2001

Street performer / outside the Sail & Anchor Hotel / South Terrace / 2001

Busker / Market Lane / Early 90's

Parade / Freo Festival / Market Street / 2000

Cafè / South Terrace / 2001

Busker / South Terrace / Late 90's

Sitar player / outside the Fremantle Markets / Late 90's

Trumpet player / South Terrace / 2001

Princess May Park / 2001

Christmas billboards / High Street Mall / 2001

Tattoo / Marine Parade / Mid 90's

Biker / Essex Street / 2001

72

St John's Square / Late 90's

Market Street / 2000

Debutante / Blessing of the fleet / 2000

Black Madonna procession / Cantonment Street / 2001

Café / South Terrace / 2000

Performers / Freo Festival / High Street / 2000

Cafè / South Terrace / 2001

Street party / South Terrace / Mid 90's

Brass band / Black Madonna procession / 2001

Buskers / South Terrace / Late 90's

Dropped bottle / High Street Mall / Mid 90's

Sword swallower / Buskers' Festival / Essex Street / 2001

Buskers / South Terrace / Mid 90's

Opera duo / near the High Street Mall / 2001

Bouncers / South Terrace / Late 90's

Street performer / South Terrace / 2001

Demonstration / Marine Parade / 2001

Near Leighton Beach / Early 90's

Looking down High Street from the mall / Mid 90's

Port Beach / Mid 90's

Port Beach / Mid 90's

Fremantle harbour / 2001

South Beach / Late 90's

Leighton Beach / Late 90's

High Street / Late 90's

Café / South Terrace / Late 90's

Opp. shop / South Terrace / Late 90's

Cafè / South Terrace / 2001

Mews Road train crossing / Late 90's

Cafè / South Terrace / Late 90's

South Terrace / 2001

Inner city footpath / 2001

Portrait sitting / outside the Sail & Anchor Hotel / South Terrace / 2001

Roadside cross / Cockburn Road / Late 90's

Drumming band / outside the Fremantle Markets / Mid 90's

Market Street / 2001

Gino's window / Market Street / 2001

Freo Festival crowd / South Terrace / 2000

South Fremantle driveway / Late 90's

Signs of life / Inner city Fremantle / Mid 90's

Photo by Jon Green 2001

BIOGRAPHY

James Kerr was born in Yorkshire, England in 1957. Migrated to Australia with family (arriving in Fremantle) in 1968. Lived in Carnarvon and Geraldton before moving to Perth for tertiary studies. B.A. English/History Curtin University 1978. Worked variously as picture framer, CES Officer, Nickel miner. Studied Film/TV at Curtin and Murdoch Universities in 1982/3. Worked on various media/TV productions, usually documentaries, as camera operator/lighting. Currently working as a freelance stills photographer/camera operator, and community house/care worker.

Back cover image: Fremantle / Inner city kerb / 2000